G000108007

# Alice in Wonderland
# V&A Diary 2022

V&A Publishing

First published by V&A Publishing, 2021
Victoria and Albert Museum
South Kensington
London SW7 2RL
vam.ac.uk/publishing

ISBN 978 1 83851 022 0

A catalogue record for this book is
available from the British Library.

Designed by Reena Kataria
Printed in China

Please note that lunar festivals marked in this
calendar may be subject to change and that
religious holiday dates can vary according to
local or regional customs.

Museum Information

Victoria and Albert Museum
South Kensington
London SW7 2RL

Visiting the Museum
vam.ac.uk/visit

What's On
vam.ac.uk/whatson

History of the Museum
vam.ac.uk/history

Search the Collections
vam.ac.uk/collections

Study Rooms
vam.ac.uk/info/study-rooms

Archives
vam.ac.uk/archives

National Art Library
vam.ac.uk/nal

V&A Shop
vam.ac.uk/shop

V&A Membership
vam.ac.uk/membership

**V&A Publishing**

Supporting the world's leading
museum of art and design,
the Victoria and Albert
Museum, London

# 2021

### JANUARY
| M | T | W | T | F | S | S |
|---|---|---|---|---|---|---|
|   |   |   |   | 1 | 2 | 3 |
| 4 | 5 | 6 | 7 | 8 | 9 | 10 |
| 11 | 12 | 13 | 14 | 15 | 16 | 17 |
| 18 | 19 | 20 | 21 | 22 | 23 | 24 |
| 25 | 26 | 27 | 28 | 29 | 30 | 31 |

### FEBRUARY
| M | T | W | T | F | S | S |
|---|---|---|---|---|---|---|
| 1 | 2 | 3 | 4 | 5 | 6 | 7 |
| 8 | 9 | 10 | 11 | 12 | 13 | 14 |
| 15 | 16 | 17 | 18 | 19 | 20 | 21 |
| 22 | 23 | 24 | 25 | 26 | 27 | 28 |

### MARCH
| M | T | W | T | F | S | S |
|---|---|---|---|---|---|---|
| 1 | 2 | 3 | 4 | 5 | 6 | 7 |
| 8 | 9 | 10 | 11 | 12 | 13 | 14 |
| 15 | 16 | 17 | 18 | 19 | 20 | 21 |
| 22 | 23 | 24 | 25 | 26 | 27 | 28 |
| 29 | 30 | 31 |   |   |   |   |

### APRIL
| M | T | W | T | F | S | S |
|---|---|---|---|---|---|---|
|   |   |   | 1 | 2 | 3 | 4 |
| 5 | 6 | 7 | 8 | 9 | 10 | 11 |
| 12 | 13 | 14 | 15 | 16 | 17 | 18 |
| 19 | 20 | 21 | 22 | 23 | 24 | 25 |
| 26 | 27 | 28 | 29 | 30 |   |   |

### MAY
| M | T | W | T | F | S | S |
|---|---|---|---|---|---|---|
|   |   |   |   |   | 1 | 2 |
| 3 | 4 | 5 | 6 | 7 | 8 | 9 |
| 10 | 11 | 12 | 13 | 14 | 15 | 16 |
| 17 | 18 | 19 | 20 | 21 | 22 | 23 |
| 24 | 25 | 26 | 27 | 28 | 29 | 30 |
| 31 |   |   |   |   |   |   |

### JUNE
| M | T | W | T | F | S | S |
|---|---|---|---|---|---|---|
|   | 1 | 2 | 3 | 4 | 5 | 6 |
| 7 | 8 | 9 | 10 | 11 | 12 | 13 |
| 14 | 15 | 16 | 17 | 18 | 19 | 20 |
| 21 | 22 | 23 | 24 | 25 | 26 | 27 |
| 28 | 29 | 30 |   |   |   |   |

### JULY
| M | T | W | T | F | S | S |
|---|---|---|---|---|---|---|
|   |   |   | 1 | 2 | 3 | 4 |
| 5 | 6 | 7 | 8 | 9 | 10 | 11 |
| 12 | 13 | 14 | 15 | 16 | 17 | 18 |
| 19 | 20 | 21 | 22 | 23 | 24 | 25 |
| 26 | 27 | 28 | 29 | 30 | 31 |   |

### AUGUST
| M | T | W | T | F | S | S |
|---|---|---|---|---|---|---|
|   |   |   |   |   |   | 1 |
| 2 | 3 | 4 | 5 | 6 | 7 | 8 |
| 9 | 10 | 11 | 12 | 13 | 14 | 15 |
| 16 | 17 | 18 | 19 | 20 | 21 | 22 |
| 23 | 24 | 25 | 26 | 27 | 28 | 29 |
| 30 | 31 |   |   |   |   |   |

### SEPTEMBER
| M | T | W | T | F | S | S |
|---|---|---|---|---|---|---|
|   |   | 1 | 2 | 3 | 4 | 5 |
| 6 | 7 | 8 | 9 | 10 | 11 | 12 |
| 13 | 14 | 15 | 16 | 17 | 18 | 19 |
| 20 | 21 | 22 | 23 | 24 | 25 | 26 |
| 27 | 28 | 29 | 30 |   |   |   |

### OCTOBER
| M | T | W | T | F | S | S |
|---|---|---|---|---|---|---|
|   |   |   |   | 1 | 2 | 3 |
| 4 | 5 | 6 | 7 | 8 | 9 | 10 |
| 11 | 12 | 13 | 14 | 15 | 16 | 17 |
| 18 | 19 | 20 | 21 | 22 | 23 | 24 |
| 25 | 26 | 27 | 28 | 29 | 30 | 31 |

### NOVEMBER
| M | T | W | T | F | S | S |
|---|---|---|---|---|---|---|
| 1 | 2 | 3 | 4 | 5 | 6 | 7 |
| 8 | 9 | 10 | 11 | 12 | 13 | 14 |
| 15 | 16 | 17 | 18 | 19 | 20 | 21 |
| 22 | 23 | 24 | 25 | 26 | 27 | 28 |
| 29 | 30 |   |   |   |   |   |

### DECEMBER
| M | T | W | T | F | S | S |
|---|---|---|---|---|---|---|
|   |   | 1 | 2 | 3 | 4 | 5 |
| 6 | 7 | 8 | 9 | 10 | 11 | 12 |
| 13 | 14 | 15 | 16 | 17 | 18 | 19 |
| 20 | 21 | 22 | 23 | 24 | 25 | 26 |
| 27 | 28 | 29 | 30 | 31 |   |   |

# 2023

### JANUARY
| M | T | W | T | F | S | S |
|---|---|---|---|---|---|---|
|   |   |   |   |   |   | 1 |
| 2 | 3 | 4 | 5 | 6 | 7 | 8 |
| 9 | 10 | 11 | 12 | 13 | 14 | 15 |
| 16 | 17 | 18 | 19 | 20 | 21 | 22 |
| 23 | 24 | 25 | 26 | 27 | 28 | 29 |
| 30 | 31 |   |   |   |   |   |

### FEBRUARY
| M | T | W | T | F | S | S |
|---|---|---|---|---|---|---|
|   |   | 1 | 2 | 3 | 4 | 5 |
| 6 | 7 | 8 | 9 | 10 | 11 | 12 |
| 13 | 14 | 15 | 16 | 17 | 18 | 19 |
| 20 | 21 | 22 | 23 | 24 | 25 | 26 |
| 27 | 28 |   |   |   |   |   |

### MARCH
| M | T | W | T | F | S | S |
|---|---|---|---|---|---|---|
|   |   | 1 | 2 | 3 | 4 | 5 |
| 6 | 7 | 8 | 9 | 10 | 11 | 12 |
| 13 | 14 | 15 | 16 | 17 | 18 | 19 |
| 20 | 21 | 22 | 23 | 24 | 25 | 26 |
| 27 | 28 | 29 | 30 | 31 |   |   |

### APRIL
| M | T | W | T | F | S | S |
|---|---|---|---|---|---|---|
|   |   |   |   |   | 1 | 2 |
| 3 | 4 | 5 | 6 | 7 | 8 | 9 |
| 10 | 11 | 12 | 13 | 14 | 15 | 16 |
| 17 | 18 | 19 | 20 | 21 | 22 | 23 |
| 24 | 25 | 26 | 27 | 28 | 29 | 30 |

### MAY
| M | T | W | T | F | S | S |
|---|---|---|---|---|---|---|
| 1 | 2 | 3 | 4 | 5 | 6 | 7 |
| 8 | 9 | 10 | 11 | 12 | 13 | 14 |
| 15 | 16 | 17 | 18 | 19 | 20 | 21 |
| 22 | 23 | 24 | 25 | 26 | 27 | 28 |
| 29 | 30 | 31 |   |   |   |   |

### JUNE
| M | T | W | T | F | S | S |
|---|---|---|---|---|---|---|
|   |   |   | 1 | 2 | 3 | 4 |
| 5 | 6 | 7 | 8 | 9 | 10 | 11 |
| 12 | 13 | 14 | 15 | 16 | 17 | 18 |
| 19 | 20 | 21 | 22 | 23 | 24 | 25 |
| 26 | 27 | 28 | 29 | 30 |   |   |

### JULY
| M | T | W | T | F | S | S |
|---|---|---|---|---|---|---|
|   |   |   |   |   | 1 | 2 |
| 3 | 4 | 5 | 6 | 7 | 8 | 9 |
| 10 | 11 | 12 | 13 | 14 | 15 | 16 |
| 17 | 18 | 19 | 20 | 21 | 22 | 23 |
| 24 | 25 | 26 | 27 | 28 | 29 | 30 |
| 31 |   |   |   |   |   |   |

### AUGUST
| M | T | W | T | F | S | S |
|---|---|---|---|---|---|---|
|   | 1 | 2 | 3 | 4 | 5 | 6 |
| 7 | 8 | 9 | 10 | 11 | 12 | 13 |
| 14 | 15 | 16 | 17 | 18 | 19 | 20 |
| 21 | 22 | 23 | 24 | 25 | 26 | 27 |
| 28 | 29 | 30 | 31 |   |   |   |

### SEPTEMBER
| M | T | W | T | F | S | S |
|---|---|---|---|---|---|---|
|   |   |   |   | 1 | 2 | 3 |
| 4 | 5 | 6 | 7 | 8 | 9 | 10 |
| 11 | 12 | 13 | 14 | 15 | 16 | 17 |
| 18 | 19 | 20 | 21 | 22 | 23 | 24 |
| 25 | 26 | 27 | 28 | 29 | 30 |   |

### OCTOBER
| M | T | W | T | F | S | S |
|---|---|---|---|---|---|---|
|   |   |   |   |   |   | 1 |
| 2 | 3 | 4 | 5 | 6 | 7 | 8 |
| 9 | 10 | 11 | 12 | 13 | 14 | 15 |
| 16 | 17 | 18 | 19 | 20 | 21 | 22 |
| 23 | 24 | 25 | 26 | 27 | 28 | 29 |
| 30 | 31 |   |   |   |   |   |

### NOVEMBER
| M | T | W | T | F | S | S |
|---|---|---|---|---|---|---|
|   |   | 1 | 2 | 3 | 4 | 5 |
| 6 | 7 | 8 | 9 | 10 | 11 | 12 |
| 13 | 14 | 15 | 16 | 17 | 18 | 19 |
| 20 | 21 | 22 | 23 | 24 | 25 | 26 |
| 27 | 28 | 29 | 30 |   |   |   |

### DECEMBER
| M | T | W | T | F | S | S |
|---|---|---|---|---|---|---|
|   |   |   |   | 1 | 2 | 3 |
| 4 | 5 | 6 | 7 | 8 | 9 | 10 |
| 11 | 12 | 13 | 14 | 15 | 16 | 17 |
| 18 | 19 | 20 | 21 | 22 | 23 | 24 |
| 25 | 26 | 27 | 28 | 29 | 30 | 31 |

MONDAY
# 20

TUESDAY
# 21

WEDNESDAY
# 22

THURSDAY
# 23

FRIDAY
# 24

**Christmas Eve**
Holiday USA

SATURDAY
# 25

**Christmas Day**
Holiday UK, IRL,
CAN, AUS, NZL

SUNDAY
# 26

**Boxing Day**
Holiday UK, AUS, NZL
**St Stephen's Day**
Holiday IRL

MONDAY
27

Holiday UK, AUS, NZL

TUESDAY
28

Holiday UK, AUS, NZL

WEDNESDAY
29

THURSDAY
30

FRIDAY
31

**New Year's Eve**
Holiday USA

SATURDAY
1

**New Year's Day**
Holiday UK, IRL,
CAN, AUS, NZL

SUNDAY
2

MONDAY

3

Holiday UK, CAN, AUS, NZL

TUESDAY

4

Holiday SCO, NZL

WEDNESDAY

5

THURSDAY

6

FRIDAY

7

SATURDAY

8

SUNDAY

9

# JANUARY

MONDAY
## 10

TUESDAY
## 11

WEDNESDAY
## 12

THURSDAY
## 13

FRIDAY
## 14

SATURDAY
## 15

SUNDAY
## 16

MONDAY
17

**Martin Luther King Jr. Day**
Holiday USA

TUESDAY
18

WEDNESDAY
19

THURSDAY
20

FRIDAY
21

SATURDAY
22

SUNDAY
23

# JANUARY

MONDAY
## 24

TUESDAY
## 25

**Robert Burns' Night**

WEDNESDAY
## 26

**Australia Day**
Holiday AUS

THURSDAY
## 27

FRIDAY
## 28

SATURDAY
## 29

SUNDAY
## 30

MONDAY
31

TUESDAY
1

Chinese New Year

WEDNESDAY
2

THURSDAY
3

FRIDAY
4

SATURDAY
5

SUNDAY
6

Waitangi Day
NZL

MONDAY
## 7

**Waitangi Day observed**
Holiday NZL

TUESDAY
## 8

WEDNESDAY
## 9

THURSDAY
## 10

FRIDAY
## 11

SATURDAY
## 12

SUNDAY
## 13

MONDAY

# 14

St Valentine's Day

TUESDAY

# 15

WEDNESDAY

# 16

THURSDAY

# 17

FRIDAY

# 18

SATURDAY

# 19

SUNDAY

# 20

## MONDAY
# 21

**Presidents' Day**
Holiday USA

## TUESDAY
# 22

## WEDNESDAY
# 23

## THURSDAY
# 24

## FRIDAY
# 25

## SATURDAY
# 26

## SUNDAY
# 27

MONDAY
# 28

TUESDAY
# 1

Shrove Tuesday
St David's Day

WEDNESDAY
# 2

THURSDAY
# 3

FRIDAY
# 4

SATURDAY
# 5

SUNDAY
# 6

MONDAY

7

TUESDAY

8

WEDNESDAY

9

THURSDAY

10

FRIDAY

11

SATURDAY

12

SUNDAY

13

**Daylight Saving Time begins**
USA, CAN

MONDAY
14

TUESDAY
15

WEDNESDAY
16

THURSDAY
17

**St Patrick's Day**
Holiday NIR, IR

FRIDAY
18

SATURDAY
19

SUNDAY
20

March Equinox

MONDAY

21

TUESDAY

22

WEDNESDAY

23

THURSDAY

24

FRIDAY

25

SATURDAY

26

SUNDAY

27

Mother's Day
UK
**British Summer Time begins**

MONDAY
# 28

TUESDAY
# 29

WEDNESDAY
# 30

THURSDAY
# 31

FRIDAY
# 1

SATURDAY
# 2

SUNDAY
# 3

First day of Ramadan
Daylight Saving Time ends
AUS, NZL

# APRIL

MONDAY
## 4

TUESDAY
## 5

WEDNESDAY
## 6

THURSDAY
## 7

FRIDAY
## 8

SATURDAY
## 9

SUNDAY
## 10

# APRIL

MONDAY
## 11

TUESDAY
## 12

WEDNESDAY
## 13

THURSDAY
## 14

FRIDAY
## 15

**Good Friday**
Holiday UK, CAN,
AUS, NZL
**First day of Passover**

SATURDAY
## 16

SUNDAY
## 17

**Easter Sunday**

MONDAY
# 18

**Easter Monday**
Holiday UK (not SCO), IRL,
CAN (many regions), AUS, NZL

TUESDAY
# 19

WEDNESDAY
# 20

THURSDAY
# 21

FRIDAY
# 22

SATURDAY
# 23

**St George's Day**
**Last day of Passover**

SUNDAY
# 24

MONDAY
# 25
**ANZAC Day**
Holiday AUS, NZL

TUESDAY
# 26

WEDNESDAY
# 27

THURSDAY
# 28

FRIDAY
# 29

SATURDAY
# 30

SUNDAY
# 1
Last day of Ramadan

MONDAY

# 2

**Early May Bank Holiday**
UK, IRL

TUESDAY

# 3

WEDNESDAY

# 4

THURSDAY

# 5

FRIDAY

# 6

SATURDAY

# 7

SUNDAY

# 8

**Mother's Day**
USA, CAN, AUS, NZL

MONDAY
9

TUESDAY
10

WEDNESDAY
11

THURSDAY
12

FRIDAY
13

SATURDAY
14

SUNDAY
15

# MAY

MONDAY
## 16

TUESDAY
## 17

WEDNESDAY
## 18

THURSDAY
## 19

FRIDAY
## 20

SATURDAY
## 21

SUNDAY
## 22

MONDAY
**23**

)

**Victoria Day**
Holiday CAN (many regions)

TUESDAY
**24**

WEDNESDAY
**25**

THURSDAY
**26**

FRIDAY
**27**

SATURDAY
**28**

SUNDAY
**29**

MONDAY

# 30

**Memorial Day**
Holiday USA

TUESDAY

# 31

WEDNESDAY

# 1

THURSDAY

# 2

**Spring Bank Holiday**
UK

FRIDAY

# 3

**Queen's Platinum Jubilee**
Holiday UK

SATURDAY

# 4

SUNDAY

# 5

MONDAY
# 6

**June Bank Holiday**
IRL
**Queen's Birthday**
Holiday NZL

TUESDAY
# 7

WEDNESDAY
# 8

THURSDAY
# 9

FRIDAY
# 10

SATURDAY
# 11

SUNDAY
# 12

# JUNE

MONDAY
## 13

TUESDAY
## 14

WEDNESDAY
## 15

THURSDAY
## 16

FRIDAY
## 17

SATURDAY
## 18

SUNDAY
## 19

**Father's Day**
UK, IRL, USA, CAN

MONDAY

# 20

TUESDAY

# 21

June Solstice

WEDNESDAY

# 22

THURSDAY

# 23

FRIDAY

# 24

SATURDAY

# 25

SUNDAY

# 26

MONDAY
27

TUESDAY
28

WEDNESDAY
29

THURSDAY
30

FRIDAY
1

**Canada Day**
Holiday CAN

SATURDAY
2

SUNDAY
3

MONDAY

## 4

**Independence Day**
Holiday USA

TUESDAY

## 5

WEDNESDAY

## 6

THURSDAY

## 7

FRIDAY

## 8

SATURDAY

## 9

SUNDAY

## 10

# JULY

MONDAY
## 11

TUESDAY
## 12

**Battle of the Boyne**
Holiday NIR

WEDNESDAY
## 13

THURSDAY
## 14

FRIDAY
## 15

SATURDAY
## 16

SUNDAY
## 17

MONDAY

18

TUESDAY

19

WEDNESDAY

20

THURSDAY

21

FRIDAY

22

SATURDAY

23

SUNDAY

24

# JULY

MONDAY
## 25

TUESDAY
## 26

WEDNESDAY
## 27

THURSDAY
## 28

FRIDAY
## 29

SATURDAY
## 30

Islamic New Year

SUNDAY
## 31

MONDAY

1

**Summer Bank Holiday**
SCO, IRL
**Civic Holiday**
CAN

TUESDAY

2

WEDNESDAY

3

THURSDAY

4

FRIDAY

5

SATURDAY

6

SUNDAY

7

# AUGUST

MONDAY
## 8

TUESDAY
## 9

WEDNESDAY
## 10

THURSDAY
## 11

FRIDAY
## 12

SATURDAY
## 13

SUNDAY
## 14

3289

3290

3291

3292

3293

3294

3295

3296

3297

3298

3299

3300½

3301½

3302½
BEST ENGLISH CHINA.

3303½

AUGUST

MONDAY
15

TUESDAY
16

WEDNESDAY
17

THURSDAY
18

FRIDAY
19

SATURDAY
20

SUNDAY
21

MONDAY
## 22

TUESDAY
## 23

WEDNESDAY
## 24

THURSDAY
## 25

FRIDAY
## 26

SATURDAY
## 27

SUNDAY
## 28

MONDAY
# 29

**Summer Bank Holiday**
UK (not SCO)

TUESDAY
# 30

WEDNESDAY
# 31

THURSDAY
# 1

FRIDAY
# 2

SATURDAY
# 3

SUNDAY
# 4

**Father's Day**
AUS, NZL

# SEPTEMBER

MONDAY

## 5

**Labour Day**
Holiday USA, CAN

TUESDAY

## 6

WEDNESDAY

## 7

THURSDAY

## 8

FRIDAY

## 9

SATURDAY

## 10

SUNDAY

## 11

MONDAY
12

TUESDAY
13

WEDNESDAY
14

THURSDAY
15

FRIDAY
16

SATURDAY
17

SUNDAY
18

# SEPTEMBER

MONDAY
## 19

TUESDAY
## 20

WEDNESDAY
## 21

THURSDAY
## 22

FRIDAY
## 23

September Equinox

SATURDAY
## 24

SUNDAY
## 25

Daylight Saving Time begins
NZL

MONDAY
26

TUESDAY
27

WEDNESDAY
28

THURSDAY
29

FRIDAY
30

SATURDAY
1

SUNDAY
2

**Daylight Saving Time begins**
AUS

MONDAY

3

TUESDAY

4

WEDNESDAY

5

Yom Kippur

THURSDAY

6

FRIDAY

7

SATURDAY

8

SUNDAY

9

**Columbus Day**
Holiday most of USA
**Thanksgiving Day**
Holiday CAN (many regions)

MONDAY
10

TUESDAY
11

WEDNESDAY
12

THURSDAY
13

FRIDAY
14

SATURDAY
15

SUNDAY
16

# OCTOBER

MONDAY
## 17

TUESDAY
## 18

WEDNESDAY
## 19

THURSDAY
## 20

FRIDAY
## 21

SATURDAY
## 22

SUNDAY
## 23

MONDAY
24

Diwali
Labour Day
Holiday NZL

TUESDAY
25

WEDNESDAY
26

THURSDAY
27

FRIDAY
28

SATURDAY
29

SUNDAY
30

British Summer Time ends

MONDAY

# 31

Hallowe'en
October Bank Holiday
IRL

TUESDAY

# 1

WEDNESDAY

# 2

THURSDAY

# 3

FRIDAY

# 4

SATURDAY

# 5

Guy Fawkes Night

SUNDAY

# 6

Daylight Saving Time ends
USA, CAN

MONDAY

7

TUESDAY

8

WEDNESDAY

9

THURSDAY

10

FRIDAY

11

**Veterans Day**
Holiday USA
**Remembrance Day**
Holiday CAN (many regions)

SATURDAY

12

SUNDAY

13

**Remembrance Sunday**
UK

# NOVEMBER

MONDAY
## 14

TUESDAY
## 15

WEDNESDAY
## 16

THURSDAY
## 17

FRIDAY
## 18

SATURDAY
## 19

SUNDAY
## 20

MONDAY
# 21

TUESDAY
# 22

WEDNESDAY
# 23

THURSDAY
# 24

**Thanksgiving**
Holiday USA

FRIDAY
# 25

SATURDAY
# 26

SUNDAY
# 27

**First Day of Advent**

MONDAY
# 28

TUESDAY
# 29

WEDNESDAY
# 30

**St Andrew's Day**
Holiday SCO

THURSDAY
# 1

FRIDAY
# 2

SATURDAY
# 3

SUNDAY
# 4

MONDAY
5

TUESDAY
6

WEDNESDAY
7

THURSDAY
8

FRIDAY
9

SATURDAY
10

SUNDAY
11

# DECEMBER

MONDAY
## 12

TUESDAY
## 13

WEDNESDAY
## 14

THURSDAY
## 15

FRIDAY
## 16

SATURDAY
## 17

SUNDAY
## 18

MONDAY
# 19

TUESDAY
# 20

WEDNESDAY
# 21

December Solstice

THURSDAY
# 22

FRIDAY
# 23

SATURDAY
# 24

**Christmas Eve**
Holiday USA

SUNDAY
# 25

**Christmas Day**
Holiday UK, IRL,
CAN, AUS, NZL

# DECEMBER / JANUARY

## MONDAY
# 26

**Boxing Day**
Holiday UK, IRL, USA,
CAN (many regions),
AUS (many regions), NZL

## TUESDAY
# 27

Holiday UK, AUS

## WEDNESDAY
# 28

## THURSDAY
# 29

## FRIDAY
# 30

## SATURDAY
# 31

New Year's Eve

## SUNDAY
# 1

**New Year's Day**
Holiday UK, IRL,
CAN, AUS, NZL

# Illustrations

Illustrations taken from *Alice's Adventures in Wonderland* by Lewis Carroll, engraved by Dalziel Brothers after John Tenniel, 1885 edition. National Art Library, V&A: 38041803021831. (Backgrounds have been cleaned and some of the images have been cropped.)

Objects paired with them come from the V&A collections. Details, including museum numbers, are given below. Further information about the objects and the collections can be found at vam.ac.uk/collections.

**Watch**
Enamelled copper gilt case
Signed 'Pierre Duhamel'
Switzerland (Geneva), 1680
V&A: 2371-1855

**Pendant with locket and key**
Gold set with coloured stones
Britain, c.1840
V&A: M.6-1986

**Bottle and stopper**
Glass with machine-threaded decoration
Britain, c.1890
V&A: CIRC.298A-1967

**Fan**
Painted vellum with ivory
Probably France, c.1700–20
V&A: T.384-1985

**Eye miniature**
Painting, with two diamond 'tears'; frame set with 20 pearls
Probably Britain, c.1790–1820
V&A: P.56-1977

**Sliding door paper** (detail)
Japan, 19th century
V&A: E.161-1955

**Tile panel** (detail)
Earthenware, painted in green enamel on white slip ground
William De Morgan, Fulham Factory
Britain (London), c.1888–98
V&A: C.55A-1984

**Bed hanging** (detail)
Painted and dyed cotton chintz
India (Coromandel Coast), early 18th century
V&A: IS.2-1967

**Pendant in the form of a lizard**
Enamelled gold set with pearls and an emerald
Europe, late 16th century
V&A: M.537-1910

**Salver** (detail)
Silver-gilt
Paul de Lamerie
Britain (London), 1741–2
V&A: Loan:Gilbert.729-2008

**Flowers with a butterfly and a caterpillar**
Plate from an illustrated book of botanical prints by Maria Sibylla Merian
Published by J.F. Bernard, Amsterdam, 1730
V&A: 38041800554677

**The lifecycle of a butterfly**
Intaglio print on paper, hand-coloured
Published by F.P. Nodder & Co., London, 1790
V&A: 29638:219

**Raja Ajmat Dev of Mankot smoking a hookah**
Opaque watercolour and gold on paper
India (Mankot), c.1730
V&A: IS.23-1974

**Frog tile**
Earthenware painted in over-glaze blue and yellow
Minton & Co.
Britian (Stoke-on-Trent), c.1875
V&A: C.183D-1976

**Devonshire Hunting Tapestry** (detail)
Tapestry woven with wool
Netherlands (south), 1425–30
V&A: T.204-1957

**Piglet dummy board**
Oil on wood
Britain, c.1750–1800
V&A: W.81-1926

**Drinking vessel in the form of a cat**
Tin-glazed earthenware
Britain (London), 1676
V&A: 414:821-1885

**Cups and saucers** (detail)
From The Silber & Fleming Glass & China Book
Britain, 19th–20th century
V&A: A.20.16

**'Rosamund' wallpaper frieze** (detail)
Colour woodblock print on paper
Designed by Walter R.W.S. Crane for Jeffrey & Co.
Britain, 1908
V&A: E.1847-1934